For _____

DAD!

I LOVE YOU BECAUSE...

25 Big (and Little) Ways You're the Best

Hey, Dad! I love you because . . .

Without you, I probably wouldn't have

_____.

Because . . .

Going

_____

with you never gets old.

And because . . .

You're such an

outstanding mix of

_____

and

_____.

Double high fives for you because . . . .

You really make me

want to up my

_____

game.

Oh yeah, and because . . .

You always

_____,

and never

_____.

And for that I'm truly

_____.

6

To me, you're #1 because . . .

When it comes to

_____,

I'm pretty sure you're

a genius.

Also because . . .

One of my favorite

memories (ever!) is when we

_____.

8

I respect you
so much, Dad,
because . . .

Your

_____

made me a better

_____.

9

You're kind
of my hero
because . . .

You know so much about

_____.

10

And especially because . . .

Okay, fine! I've got to admit you were right about

_____.

I really respect you because . . .

You've always

_____

me to

_____.

But also because . . .

If you were a superhero,
your superpower would be

_____.

13

I know I hit
the dad-jackpot
because ...

You let me

_____,

which taught me a lot.

14

Love ya so
much, Pops!
And not just
because . . .

Thanks to you, I've got excellent taste in

_____.

15

Because honestly . . .

You have the coolest

_____

of any dad out there.

16

And obviously because . . .

You still love me, even

when I'm

_____ .

Thank god you're my dad because . . .

You showed me how to

_____.

18

Not to mention because . . .

Your dedication to

_____

never ceases to amaze me.

19

You win the
Rad Dad Award
because . . .

You somehow

magically make

_____

look easy.

20

And because . . .

If you were a rock and roll

anthem, you'd be

" _____ "

21

I'm grateful to you for so many reasons, like because . . .

It makes my heart

go "aw!" when you

_____

me.

22

I love you because . . .

You're the most

_____

dad I know.

Because!
Because!
Because!

I really do value your

_____

even if sometimes

it seems like

_____.

24

Did I mention
I'm glad you're
my dad?
Because . . .

Hearing your stories about

_____

is a real hoot.

25

And, last but
not least,
because . . .

Your

_____

skills are unrivaled in

the infinite galaxy of dads.

I love you.

YEAH,
DAD!

Created, published, and distributed by Knock Knock
11111 Jefferson Blvd. #5167
Culver City, CA 90231
knockknockstuff.com
Knock Knock is a registered trademark of Knock Knock LLC
Fill in the Love is a registered trademark of Knock Knock LLC

ISBN: 978–168349265–8   UPC: 825703–50267–1

20 19 18 17 16 15 14 13 12 11 10 9 8 7 6 5 4 3 2 1